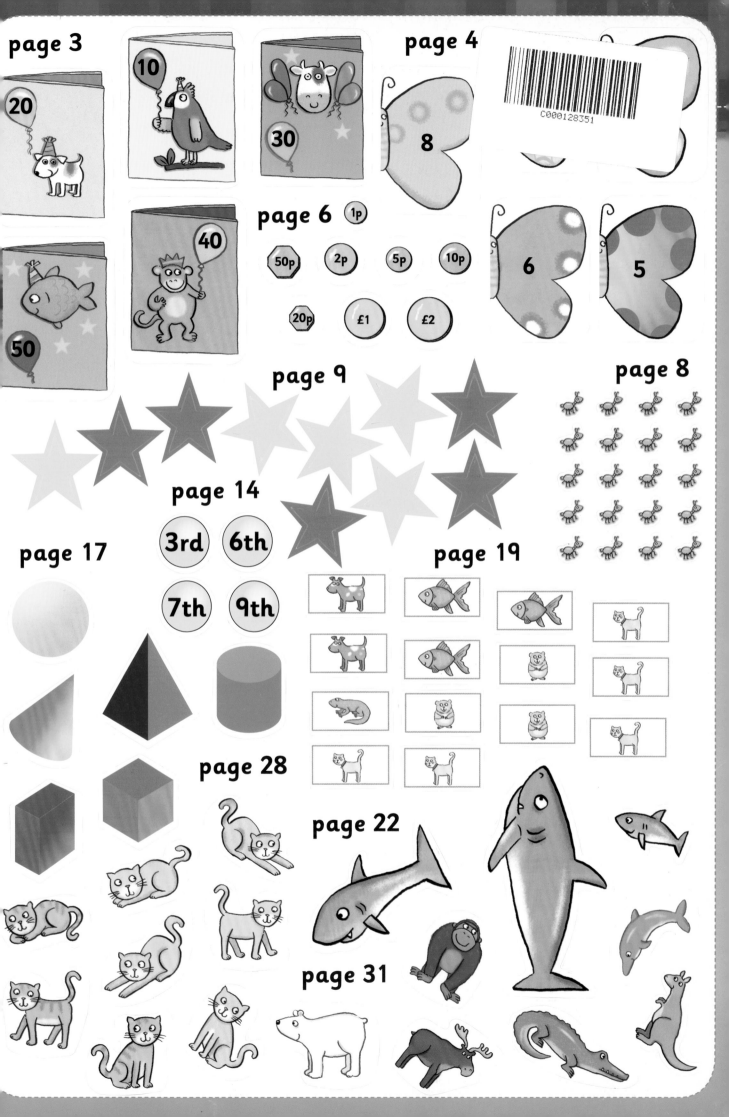

Maths

Leap Ahead Workbook

Home learning made fun

5-6 years

Leap Ahead

Key Stage 1

igloobooks

Counting to 20

Look at all of these leopards. Estimate how many spots they have, then count the spots to see if you were right.

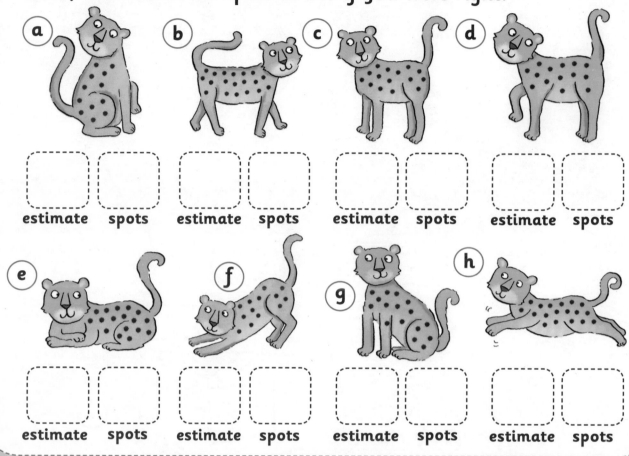

(a) estimate ☐ spots ☐ (b) estimate ☐ spots ☐ (c) estimate ☐ spots ☐ (d) estimate ☐ spots ☐

(e) estimate ☐ spots ☐ (f) estimate ☐ spots ☐ (g) estimate ☐ spots ☐ (h) estimate ☐ spots ☐

How many bugs are in this tank? ☐

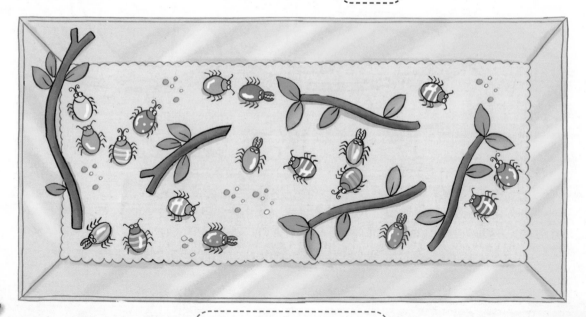

Answers on page 32

Teen Numbers and Words

Join each mouse to the correct mouse hole.

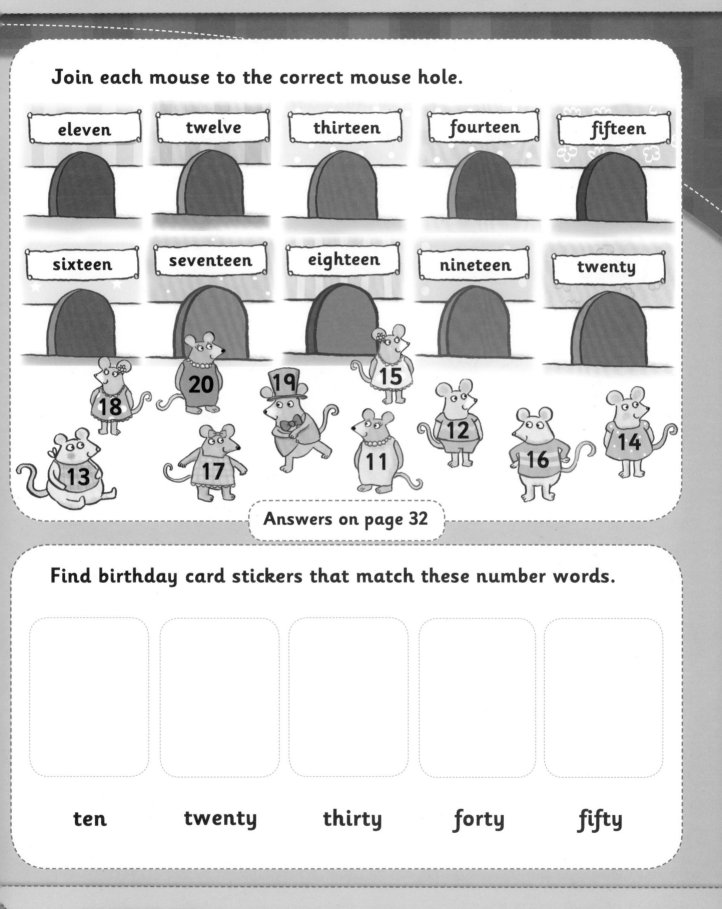

| eleven | twelve | thirteen | fourteen | fifteen |
| sixteen | seventeen | eighteen | nineteen | twenty |

Answers on page 32

Find birthday card stickers that match these number words.

ten   twenty   thirty   forty   fifty

PARENT TIP: Children should be able to count consistently to 20 and beyond. Make sure they say the numbers and point to each object being counted. Also practise counting things that cannot be touched, such as footsteps, jumps and claps, as well as objects out of reach.

Make 10

Find the correct butterfly sticker to complete each butterfly. The numbers on both wings must add up to 10.

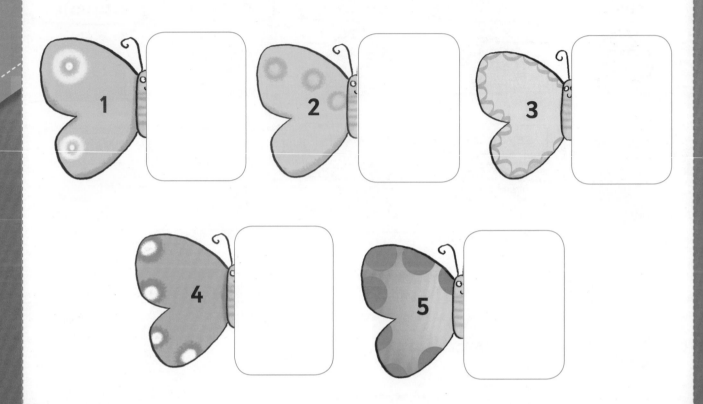

Complete these number sums.

(a) 1 + ⬚ = 10

(b) 2 + ⬚ = 10

(c) 3 + ⬚ = 10

(d) 4 + ⬚ = 10

(e) 5 + ⬚ = 10

(f) 9 + ⬚ = 10

(g) 8 + ⬚ = 10

(h) 7 + ⬚ = 10

(i) 6 + ⬚ = 10

(j) 10 + ⬚ = 10

Answers on page 32

Choose pairs of beehives that have a total of 20 bees when added together. Join them with a line.

Answers on page 32

Colour pairs to make 20. Use different colours for each pair.

1	2	3	4	5	6	7	8	9
11	12	13	14	15	16	17	18	19

PARENT TIP: Knowing pairs that total 10 and using these to calculate pairs that total 20 is very important. Why not play a game? Say "4" and your child replies with the number to add to make 10. You could also play Number Pairs Snap. Have number cards to 20 and turn them over, looking for pairs that make 10 or 20.

Money Maths

Choose coin stickers to pay for these toys.

This goat costs 6p.
Tick the coins you could use
to pay for it in each purse.

Count the money in each piggy bank.

Total = [   ] p   Total = [   ] p   Total = [   ] p

Answers on page 32

These things are for sale in the pet shop.
What is the cost of each basket of goods?

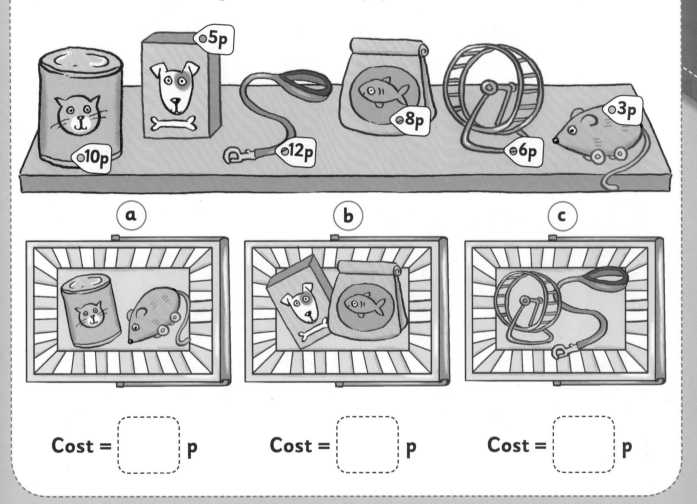

5p 8p 3p 10p 12p 6p

a **b** **c**

Cost = ⬚ p   Cost = ⬚ p   Cost = ⬚ p

Rory buys a new dog lead. He has 20p.
How much change will he get?   Change = ⬚ p

Carly buys some dog biscuits. She has 20p.
How much change will she get?   Change = ⬚ p

Answers on page 32

Missing Number Puzzles

These tanks have room for more ants. Count how many ants are already inside and work out how many extra can fit. Write the answers in the boxes.

b

Holds 6 ants

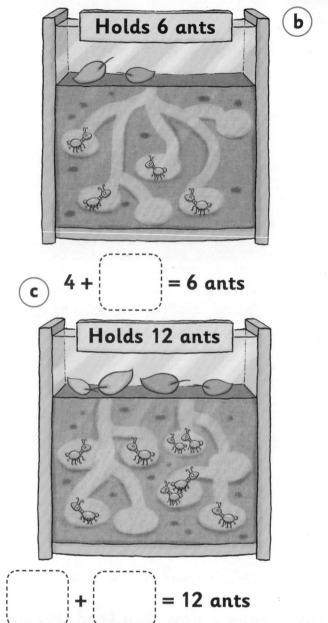

a

Holds 20 ants

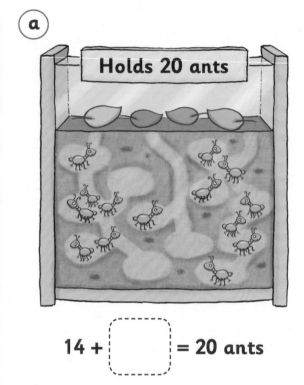

c   4 + ☐ = 6 ants

14 + ☐ = 20 ants

Holds 12 ants

☐ + ☐ = 12 ants

Find the ant stickers on the sticker sheet. Use the stickers to add more ants to the tank. How many do you need to make 20?

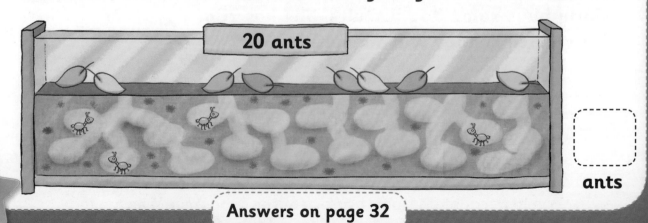

20 ants

☐

ants

Answers on page 32

Repeating Patterns

Here are 3 snakes. Colour the patterns on their bodies. Each snake must look different.

These zoo animals have special identity numbers. Carry on the repeating number patterns.

1-2-1-2-1- ☐ ☐ ☐

3-6-3-6-3- ☐ ☐ ☐

2-4-6-2-4- ☐ ☐ ☐

Answers on page 32

Choose different coloured star stickers and make a repeating colour pattern.

PARENT TIP: Arrange toys and household objects into repeating patterns, such as spoon-fork-spoon-fork, on the dinner table. See if your child can describe the part of the pattern that repeats and then continue it themselves.

9

Counting On to Add

Help the monkeys cross the bridges. Count on from the start number to work out which number each monkey lands on.

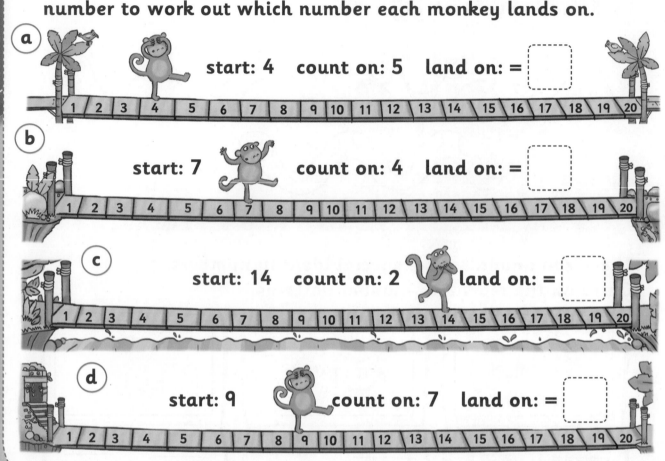

a start: 4   count on: 5   land on: =

1 2 3 4 5 6 7 8 9 10 11 12 13 14 15 16 17 18 19 20

b start: 7   count on: 4   land on: =

1 2 3 4 5 6 7 8 9 10 11 12 13 14 15 16 17 18 19 20

c start: 14   count on: 2   land on: =

1 2 3 4 5 6 7 8 9 10 11 12 13 14 15 16 17 18 19 20

d start: 9   count on: 7   land on: =

1 2 3 4 5 6 7 8 9 10 11 12 13 14 15 16 17 18 19 20

8 monkeys are already inside the party. Another 6 have arrived. How many does that make in total?

8 monkeys inside

monkeys

10

Answers on page 32

2D Shapes

Draw the other half of each shape. Match them to their names.

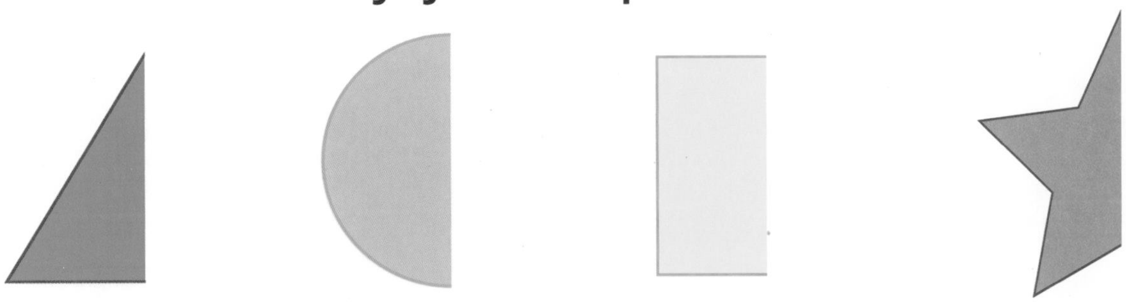

Star Square Triangle Circle

Draw 2 different 4-sided shapes.

Circle and count the points on this star.
How many sides does it have?

Points

Sides

Answers on page 32

PARENT TIP: Your child must learn to count on from different numbers when adding. Practise putting the largest number in your head, then counting on, e.g. put 8 in your head (mime putting a hat on), then count on 3, saying, "8... 9, 10, 11". Keep track of the 3 that your child has counted on, by raising one finger for each number said.

Time

Number these months to show the correct order. One has been done for you.

January = 1	December = ☐	November = ☐
July = ☐	September = ☐	March = ☐
April = ☐	June = ☐	August = ☐
October = ☐	February = ☐	May = ☐

Name a summer month ....

Name a winter month ....

Answers on page 32

Look at these daily events.
Write 'm' below the events that happen in the morning.
Write 'a' below the events that happen in the afternoon.
Write 'n' below the events that happen at night.

PARENT TIP: Refer to o'clock and half-past times and talk about the position of the 'hands' on an analogue clock. Create a visual timetable of things that happen on a school day or weekend and refer to it during the course of the day. Write times alongside events if appropriate.

The zookeeper is looking after the animals. Write down the time in words that he does each job. One has been done for you.

9 o'clock

Answers on page 32

Draw the hands on these clocks to show times of the special events at the zoo.

Seal show
9 o'clock

Bird display
half past 1

Reptile talk
3 o'clock

Ride an elephant
half past 10

Feed a snake
half past 4

13

Ordinal Numbers

Look at this line of animals waiting to be fed.
The elephant is 1st. Put position stickers next to the animals that are 3rd, 6th, 7th and 9th in the line.

1st

What position are the following animals?

giraffe ☐   zebra ☐   penguin ☐

Colour the feeding plates in this order:
Red: 1st, 4th
Green: 2nd, 5th
Blue: 3rd, 6th

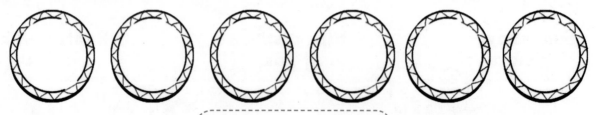

Answers on page 32

PARENT TIP: Use ordinal numbers (1st, 2nd, 3rd, etc.) to describe positions and 'taking turns' at home, e.g. Jamie can get a drink first, then Amanda second. Set up races with friends and award 1st, 2nd and 3rd place medals and certificates.

Odds and Evens

Colour numbers 1, 3 and 5 in red. Carry on colouring every other number in red.

1	2	3	4	5	6	7	8	9	10
11	12	13	14	15	16	17	18	19	20

The red numbers are odd numbers.
The other numbers are even numbers.

Decide if the number of squares in each shape is odd or even by counting how many squares are in each shape. Write 'odd' or 'even' under each one. What do you notice?

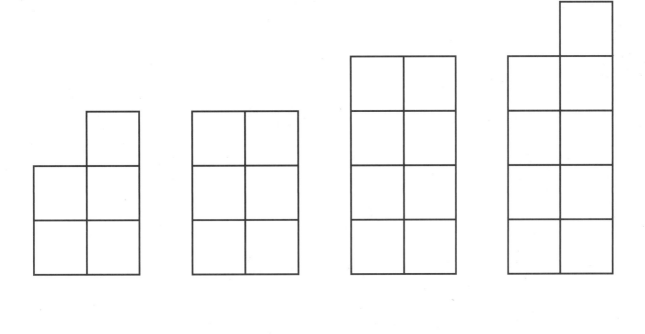

....

Counting Back

This bee flies from flower to flower. Follow the instructions and count back to see where she lands.

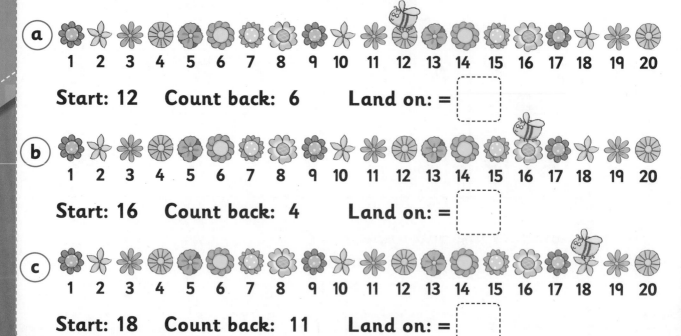

(a) 1 2 3 4 5 6 7 8 9 10 11 12 13 14 15 16 17 18 19 20

Start: 12   Count back: 6   Land on: = ☐

(b) 1 2 3 4 5 6 7 8 9 10 11 12 13 14 15 16 17 18 19 20

Start: 16   Count back: 4   Land on: = ☐

(c) 1 2 3 4 5 6 7 8 9 10 11 12 13 14 15 16 17 18 19 20

Start: 18   Count back: 11   Land on: = ☐

There were 14 bees in this hive. 7 have flown out.
How many are left inside?

Answers on page 32

☐ bees

PARENT TIP: Counting back to find answers to subtractions is difficult for children. Use fingers to keep track of the numbers counted back, so they know when to stop. Draw a number track on the garden path with chalk and practise jumping back in 1s from different starting points.

16

3D Shapes

Here is a set of 3D shapes. Colour the shapes below to match.

Find the 3D shape stickers and put them in the correct place on this chart.

Shapes that roll	Shapes that do not roll

PARENT TIP: Find some solid 3D shapes, e.g. tissue box for cuboid, baked bean tin for cylinder, dice for cube. Count the faces, edges and vertices. Describe shapes to each other. Can you guess the shape from its description?

Pictograms

Max and Harry went rock-pooling and collected lots of sea creatures. This pictogram shows what they caught.

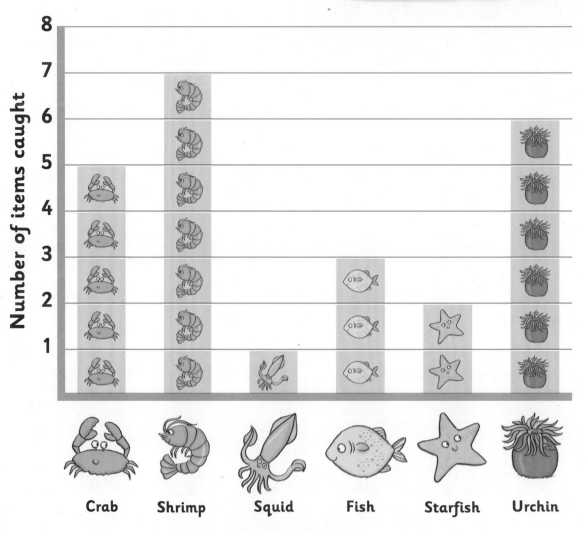

1. How many crabs did they catch? ....

2. Did they catch any fish? How many? ....

3. Which creature did they catch 6 of? ....

4. How many creatures did they catch altogether? ....

Answers on page 32

Amanda asked her friends what pets they owned. She put the information in a chart.

Pet	Number of friends who have one
Fish	3
Dog	2
Cat	5
Lizard	1
Hamster	3

1. Which is the most common pet?

....

2. How many friends own a dog?

....

3. Which pet does only 1 friend own?

....

Answers on page 32

Put pet stickers on the pictogram to show Amanda's results.

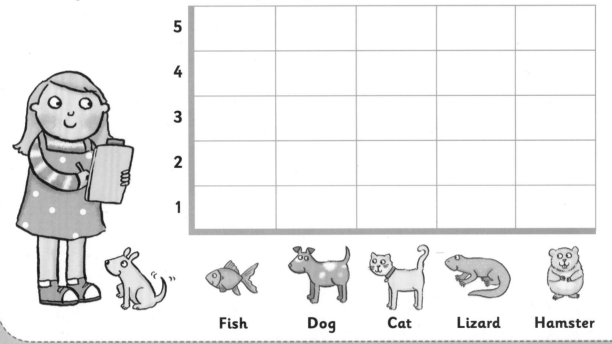

Fish   Dog   Cat   Lizard   Hamster

PARENT TIP: Looking at information collected and presented in different ways is very important. Write a list of five colours, then ask family and friends to choose their favourite. Record the information in a chart and then show it as a pictogram.

19

Numbers to 50

Write the missing numbers on these snakes.

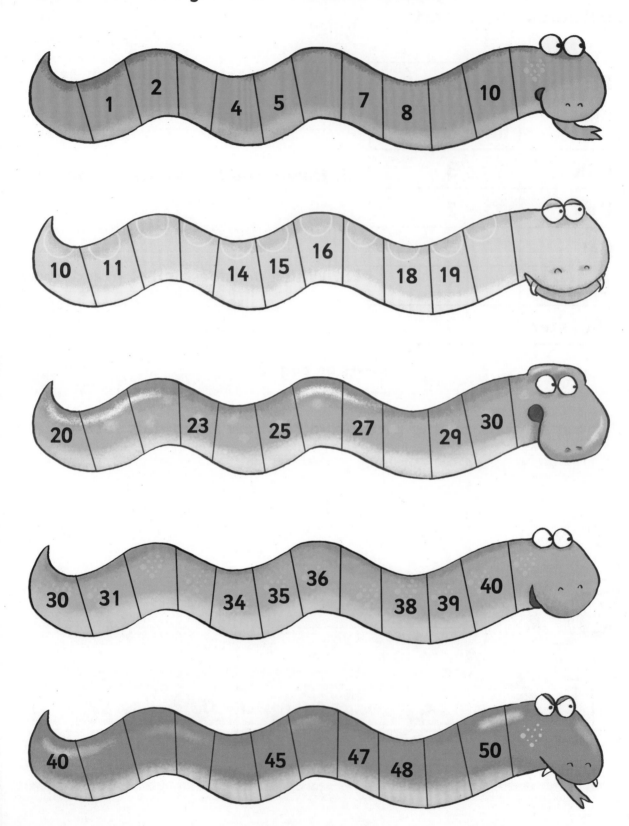

Complete this picture joining the numbers in order.

PARENT TIP: Chanting numbers in order to 50 and beyond is very important. Children need to become familiar with the pattern that repeats each ten. Initially they will need help to 'bridge' to the next ten. Help them over the next ten by chanting together, "30, 31, 32..." and then leave them to continue again by themselves.

Measuring

These divers are learning about sharks. Use a ruler to measure the length of each shark. Write the lengths in the boxes in centimetres, then circle the longest shark.

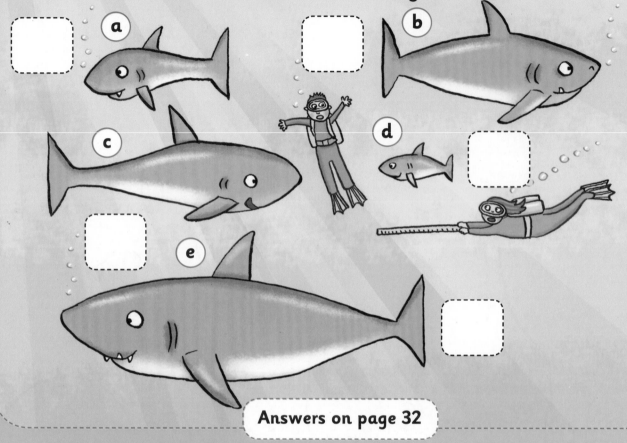

Answers on page 32

Choose the shark stickers that measure 2cm, 4cm and 6cm. Stick them here in order, from shortest to longest.

Now draw your own shark which is 5cm in length.

The divers have weighed the sharks to find the heaviest one. Look at the number that each scale is pointing to and write the weights down as words.

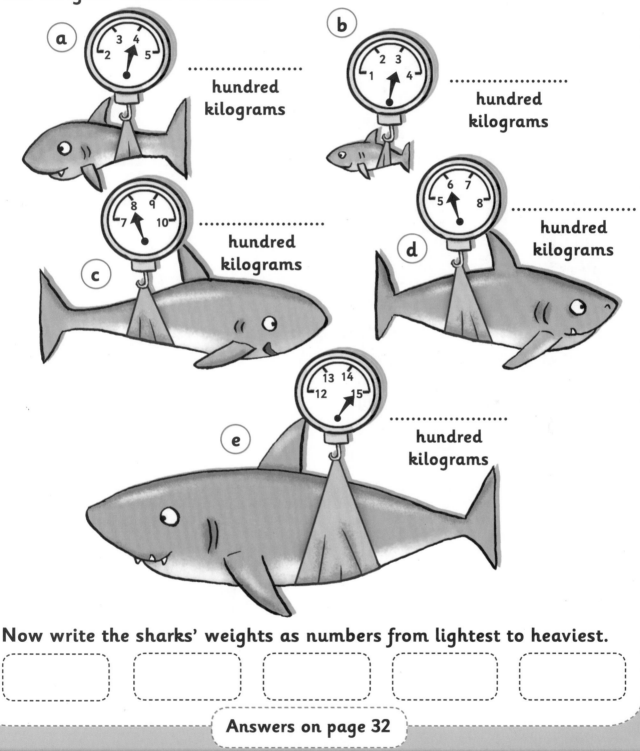

a .... hundred kilograms

b .... hundred kilograms

c .... hundred kilograms

d .... hundred kilograms

e .... hundred kilograms

Now write the sharks' weights as numbers from lightest to heaviest.

Answers on page 32

PARENT TIP: Look round the home together to find the shortest, the longest, the tallest, the heaviest and the lightest objects. Hold two items directly against each other to compare their lengths and then hold one in each hand to compare their weights. Begin to use rulers and tape measures to measure objects to the nearest whole centimetre.

Doubling

Read the sentences and then complete the sums below.

Farmer Ted has 2 fields with 3 sheep in each field.

$2 \times 3 = \boxed{}$

Farmer Jack has 2 stables with 4 horses in each stable.

$2 \times 4 = \boxed{}$

Farmer Claire has 2 ponds with 6 ducks on each pond.

$2 \times 6 = \boxed{}$

Join each number to its double.

5   9   4   14

7   2   10   18

Answers on page 32

PARENT TIP: Choose a number to double, e.g. 3. Now slowly turn over cards in a playing card set. The first to spot the double shouts, "Stop!" and wins those cards. Choose a different number and continue the game. Remove cards not in play, e.g. Jack, Queen, King and Aces.

Counting in 2s, 5s and 10s

How many frogs? Count in 2s to find out.

How many fish? Count in 5s to find out.

How many bugs? Count in 10s to find out.

10	**10**	**10**	**10**	

Complete these number sequences.

2	4		8			14

5		15		25		35

10	20		40		60	

Answers on page 32

Counting to 100

Look at the numbers the birds are holding, then find them on the number square on page 27.

Number Order

1	2	3	4	5	6	7	8	9	10
11	12	13	14	15	16	17	18	19	20
21	22	23	24	25	26	27	28	29	30
31	32	33	34	35	36	37	38	39	40
41	42	43	44	45	46	47	48	49	50
51	52	53	54	55	56	57	58	59	60
61	62	63	64	65	66	67	68	69	70
71	72	73	74	75	76	77	78	79	80
81	82	83	84	85	86	87	88	89	90
91	92	93	94	95	96	97	98	99	100

Use the number square to answer these answers.

1. What is 3 more than 40?

2. What is 10 more than 50?

3. What is 5 more than 66?

4. What is 2 less than 80?

5. What is 6 less than 38?

6. What is 4 less than 100?

PARENT TIP: Knowing the order of numbers to 100 and finding them on number grids and number lines is a key skill. Practise this by looking for given numbers on tape measures and measuring jugs in the home. Use vocabulary, such as 'before' and 'after', to describe the position of specific numbers in relation to others.

Halves and Quarters

Here are 6 rabbits. Half of the group live in each rabbit hutch. Join the rabbits to their hutches.

Find 8 kitten stickers. Put half of the 8 stickers in each basket.

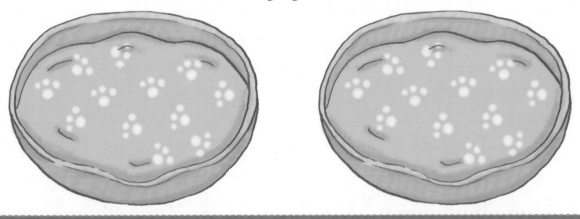

Here is a tank with 10 fish. Colour half of them green and half of them orange. How many are orange?

Answers on page 32

PARENT TIP: Children tend to develop an intuitive understanding of 'half' through sharing. Highlight these 'sharing between two' opportunities and clarify that it needs to be fair and both people need to get the same number. Practise finding half of a number of objects, by sharing them out. Then ask, "how many do we each have?"

Look at the group of bugs below. Circle half of the total number in each set.

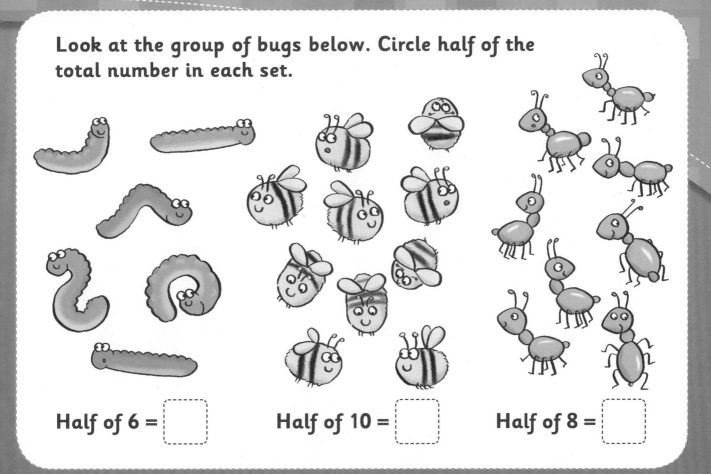

Half of 6 = ☐   Half of 10 = ☐   Half of 8 = ☐

Each child will take home a quarter of these snails. Join the snails to their new owners.

Answers on page 32

Turning

Bill the zookeeper needs to keep watch over all the animals. He stays in the centre and turns clockwise to face each group.

Fill the gaps in the table below.

Start facing	Turn	End facing
giraffes	one quarter turn	
penguins	one half turn	
tigers		giraffes
giraffes	one half turn	
monkeys		tigers
tigers	three quarter turn	
monkeys	one half turn	
giraffes	one whole turn	

Answers on page 32

Calculation Puzzles

Use the animal code to do these calculations.
Write the answers in the boxes.

a   🐬 − 🦌 = ⬚

b   🦍 − 🦘 = ⬚

c   🐊 + 🐻 = ⬚

d   🐬 + 🐻 = ⬚

Answers on page 32

Make up one addition and one subtraction sum yourself using the animal code stickers.

Answers

Page 2: Counting to 20
a – 12, b – 19, c – 15, d – 14, e – 17, f – 13,
g – 16, h – 18. There are 18 bugs in the tank.

Page 3: Teen Numbers and Words

Page 4: Make 10

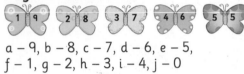

a – 9, b – 8, c – 7, d – 6, e – 5,
f – 1, g – 2, h – 3, i – 4, j – 0

Page 5: Make 20
5 + 15, 6 + 14, 7 + 13, 8 + 12, 9 + 11

Page 6: Money Maths
Purse a = 2p + 2p + 1p + 1p, Purse b = 5p + 1p
Purse c = 2p + 2p + 2p
Piggy bank a = 16p, Piggy bank b = 30p
Piggy bank c = 50p

Page 7: Money Maths (continued)
Basket a – 13p, basket b – 13p, basket c – 18p
Rory gets 8p change, Carly gets 15p change.

Page 8: Missing Number Puzzles
Ant farm a: 14 + 6 = 20 ants
Ant farm b: 4 + 2 = 6 ants
Ant farm c: 8 + 4 = 12 ants
You need to add 16 ant stickers to make 20.

Page 9: Repeating Patterns
Zebra: 1-2-1-2-1-2-1-2
Tiger: 3-6-3-6-3-6-3-6
Monkey: 2-4-6-2-4-6-2-4

Page 10: Counting On to Add
Bridge a: Monkey lands on 9, Bridge b: Monkey
lands on 11, Bridge c: Monkey lands on 16,
Bridge d: Monkey lands on 16.
There will be 14 monkeys at the party.

Page 11: 2D Shapes
The star has: 5 points and 10 sides

Page 12: Time
January – 1, February – 2, March – 3, April – 4,
May – 5, June – 6, July – 7, August – 8,
September – 9, October – 10, November – 11,
December – 12

Page 13: Time (continued)
Feed the penguins: nine o'clock, Play with the
monkeys: ten o'clock, Feed the crocodile: one o'clock
Wash the elephant: two o'clock, Feed the tiger: three
o'clock, Tidy the penguins: four o'clock

Page 14: Ordinal Numbers
3rd: Tiger, 6th: Monkey, 7th: Rhino, 9th: Lion
Giraffe: 2nd, Zebra: 5th, Penguin: 8th

Page 16: Counting Back
Bee a lands on 6, Bee b lands on 12, Bee c lands on 7.
7 bees are left inside the hive.

Page 18: Pictograms
1. 5 crabs, 2. 3 fish, 3. 6 urchins, 4. 24 creatures
Page 19: Pictograms (continued)
1. Cats are the most common pet, 2. 2 friends own
a dog, 3. Only one friend has a lizard.

Page 22: Measuring
Shark a is 4cm, shark b is 6cm, shark c is 7cm,
shark d is 2cm, shark e is 10cm
Page 23: Measuring (continued)
a = four hundred kg, b = three hundred kg,
c = eight hundred kg, d = six hundred kg,
e = fifteen hundred kg.
Lightest to heaviest: b – (300 kg), a – (400 kg),
d – (600 kg), c – (800 kg), e – (1500 kg)

Page 24: Doubling
2 x 3 = 6, 2 x 4 = 8, 2 x 6 = 12
5 – 10, 9 – 18, 7 – 14, 2 – 4

Page 25: Counting in 2s, 5s and 10s
8 frogs, 15 fish, 40 bugs
2 4 6 8 10 12 14, 5 10 15 20 25 30 35,
10 20 30 40 50 60 70

Page 27: Number order
1. 43, 2. 60, 3. 71, 4. 78, 5. 32, 6. 96

Page 28: Halves and Quarters
5 fish are orange
Page 29: Halves and Quarters (continued)
half of 6 = 3, half of 10 = 5, half of 8 = 4
Each child takes home 3 snails.

Page 30: Turning

Start facing	Turn	End facing
giraffes	one quarter turn	penguins
penguins	one half turn	tigers
tigers	one quarter turn	giraffes
giraffes	one half turn	monkeys
monkeys	one quarter turn	tigers
tigers	three quarter turn	monkeys
monkeys	one half turn	giraffes
giraffes	one whole turn	giraffes

Page 31: Calculation Puzzles
a = 2, b = 9, c = 25, d = 23